Puzzles & Quizzes

By
**E. Richard and
Linda R. Churchill**

SCHOLASTIC BOOK SERVICES
New York Toronto London Auckland Sydney Tokyo

For Sean
Who delights in being a puzzle

Copyright © 1974 by E. Richard and Linda R. Churchill. All rights reserved. Published by Scholastic Book Services, a division of Scholastic Magazines, Inc.

13 12 11 10 9 8 7 6 5 4 3 2   8 9/7 0 1 2 3/8
Printed in U.S.A.   01

1. WORD BOXES

Word Boxes have been around for hundreds of years. A completed word box reads the same across as it does downward. The answer which fits number one across is also the answer for number one down. The same is true for two, three, and four. Just follow the clues and construct half a dozen Word Boxes in this puzzle.

I

1. Halt
2. Used to mend torn paper
3. Not shut
4. Writing instruments

II

1. A compass direction
2. Repeat
3. Closed
4. Children

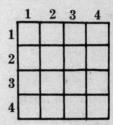

III

1. Used in winter sports
2. Great affection
3. Not odd
4. Not wanted in car fenders

IV

1. Gold comes from it
2. A thought
3. Information about world events
4. A direction

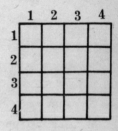

V

1. A fruit
2. Size of a surface
3. Column between ones and hundreds
4. Leisure

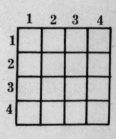

VI

1. Misplaced
2. A reed instrument
3. Made with ice cream
4. Rip

Now that you have completed the final Word Box you should be ready for the Four Square puzzle which follows.

2

2. FOUR SQUARE

A Four Square contains sixteen letters in four rows of four letters each. Each row (across) of four letters spells a four letter word. Each column (up and down) of four letters spells a four letter word, making a total of eight words in a Four Square. Follow the clues and you can't get lost.

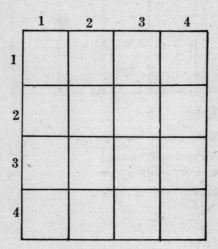

I

ACROSS

1. A number of items on a paper
2. Alone, one of a kind
3. Seen in the sky at night
4. A homonym is sum

DOWN

1. Related to lost
2. Opposite of out of
3. Hit hard
4. English spelling for tire

II

ACROSS

1. Many games use one
2. Musical instrument in reed family
3. Exclamation showing sorrow
4. Canvas cover for campers

DOWN

1. It floats (or should!)
2. Can
3. To allow to use but not keep
4. For fear that — ____ we forget

4

III

	1	2	3	4
1				
2				
3				
4				

ACROSS

1. Ran away
2. Not dead
3. Sung at end of hymn
4. Past tense of go

DOWN

1. An error
2. Citrus fruit
3. Not odd
4. Beginning drivers may put these in car fenders

IV

Now that you have had some experience at solving Four Squares let's change things a bit. Instead of clues for this one you will find the letters to use for each answer. Just unscramble them to spell a word which will fit into the puzzle.

ACROSS

1. D O C E
2. R A E A
3. N V S A
4. L E E S

DOWN

1. V E C A
2. R O L A
3. N E D S
4. S A E E

V

For this Four Square you'll find the words you need listed below. Just decide where they go and fit them in.

side   flat

Asia   safe

eels   eats

isle   dial

6

VI

Our final Four Square should be a snap. Eight clues and sixteen letters are listed. Follow the clues and use all the letters to fill in the Four Square. The clues may be a bit out of order but we're sure you can take care of that, especially since the starting letter is already in the puzzle.

CLUES

Lump of dirt

Body of water

Measure of land

A fruit

Striking together of hands

Elk's relative

Fancy trim

Vegetable used in soups

LETTERS TO USE

a, a, a, c, c, d, e, e, e, k, l, l, o, p, r, r

	1	2	3	4
1	C			
2				
3				
4				

3. MONKEY MATH

This puzzle is called "Monkey Math" because it has so much monkeying around in it. Just follow the clues and be sure your answer fits the space provided. Then check to be certain every answer crosses another answer correctly. All answers are written as whole numbers, of course.

ACROSS

1. Number of states plus 7½ decades
4. Largest possible three-digit number
7. Twenty pair
8. Number of legs on three baby elephants
10. Arms on seven octopuses
11. Number of teeth in a normal chicken plus 4
12. Days in four consecutive years
14. Freezing on a centigrade thermometer
15. XL − IV
17. IV + VI + III + IX + VII + VIII
19. Three score and one

8

20. One half of 4×11
21. Feet on the normal elephant
22. Year Columbus discovered America plus 1121
25. A sextet minus a trio
26. Number of U.S. Senators minus 62
28. Two score plus two decades plus two pair
29. Stars in the United States flag in 1940

DOWN

1. Hours in a day plus minutes in an hour plus seconds in a minute
2. Century in which we now live
3. Next odd number after 3
4. A trio plus a duo plus a quartet
5. A century minus half a decade
6. $1 \times 2 \times 3 \times 4 \times 5 \times 8$
8. Two baker's dozens less a dozen
9. Number of heads on 13 pushmi-pullyus
12. Weeks in a year times days in January
13. Feet in one fourth of a mile plus feet in a yard
15. One fourth of a gross
18. Three dozen plus inches in a yard
21. $XXXI \times XIV$
23. Number of tails on 42 dogs, 23 cats, and a comet

9

24. Number of months with 31 days plus days in a week
25. Square feet in 43 square yards
27. Total number of feet, heads, and tails on 14 giraffes
20. One half of 4 × 11
21. Feet on the normal elephant
22. Year Columbus discovered America plus 1121
25. A sextet minus a trio
26. Number of U.S. Senators minus 62
28. Two score plus two decades plus two pair
29. Stars in the United States flag in 1940
30. Half a millennium minus 51
32. CL + CX + LXXX + CCVII
29. Squares to fill in this puzzle
31. Letters in the authors' last name
32. Number of states in the United States bordering the Pacific Ocean

4. STAIRSTEPS

As you can see, each of the following puzzles contains a stairway. Each correct word in the puzzle adds one stairstep to that stairway. When the puzzle is completed correctly the stairsteps will spell a state name.

The clues should make it easy for you to fill in each stairstep without too much work.

I

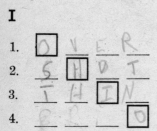

1. O V E R
2. S H U T
3. T H I N
4. H E R O

1. Not under
2. Not open
3. Not fat
4. Not a coward

11

II

1. M I N E R
2. C A N O E
3. _ _ _
4. E O I T H
5. _ _ _ _ _

1. **Mineral digger**
2. **Indians made it of birch bark**
3. **An act which breaks the law**
4. **Not back**
5. **Perhaps**

III

1. N e P H E W
2. S E C O N D
3. r e V i e W
4. F E M A L E
5. G U A R D
6. C A N A D A

1. **Your brother's (or sister's) son**
2. **A measure of time**
3. **Look over or study for a test**
4. **Not male**
5. **Sentries**
6. **Large North American nation**

IV

1. □ _ _ _ _ _ _ _
2. _ □ _ _ _ _ _ _
3. _ _ □ _ _ _ _ _
4. _ _ _ □ _ _ _ _
5. _ _ _ _ □ _ _ _
6. _ _ _ _ _ □ _ _
7. _ _ _ _ _ _ □ _

1. Style of dress
2. Shine or sparkle
3. Not straight
4. Surprise
5. Supply
6. Not inside
7. Name often given the United States

V

1. □ _ _ _ _ _ _ _
2. _ □ _ _ _ _ _ _
3. _ _ □ _ _ _ _ _
4. _ _ _ □ _ _ _ _
5. _ _ _ _ □ _ _ _
6. _ _ _ _ _ □ _ _
7. _ _ _ _ _ _ □ _
8. _ _ _ _ _ _ _ □

13

1. Money paid for use of borrowed money
2. Precious metal
3. Fish often kept as a pet
4. Helps keep many car engines cool
5. Florida Indian
6. Means of transportation
7. Southern tree with sweet smelling flowers
8. Those who teach

5. VOCABULARY CHECK

How is your vocabulary? Are you with it? Match the items at the left with their definitions at the right to see whether you are right up front or way out back.

1. Sleeping bag   Thirst aid station
2. Waffle   Napsack
3. Post office   Stamping ground
4. Suit of armor   Top secret
5. Hypodermic needle   Sick shooter
6. Tropical fish   Person with the gift of grab
7. Cannibal   Car's life story
8. Water cooler   Non-skid pancake

9. Autobiography

10. Shoplifter

11. Astronomer

12. Sorceress' time-
piece

13. Toupee

14. Mosquito

15. King's newborn
son

Night watchman

One who is fed up with
people

Flying hypodermic
needle

Knightgown

Wet pets

Witch watch

Prince of Wails

6. WHAT A NEIGHBORHOOD!

Three men, Mr. Grouch, Mr. Grump, and Mr.
Growl, lived side by side as can be seen in the
drawing below. On the same block lived Miss
Susie Smart, Miss Pamela Pleasant, and Miss
Hanna Happy. As so often happens, the three
men became quite friendly with the three wom-
en and visited them daily. As so often happens
as well, the three men became jealous of one
another. They fussed at one another until they
were not on speaking terms. They didn't even
wish to meet as they walked to and from the
women's houses. With this in mind the three
decided to build their own private sidewalks.
Each man intended to build a walk connecting
his home with each of the women's homes. In
other words, each man started building three

15

separate sidewalks from his own home. This made nine sidewalks in all. The men declared that no sidewalk would cross the sidewalk of another man, but they ran into trouble.

Can you help these three foolish men with their nine sidewalks? We can't and they can't. Can you?

Mr. Grouch	Mr. Grump	Mr. Growl

Miss Susie Smart	Miss Pamela Pleasant	Miss Hanna Happy

7. THE LOSER

Bad Luck Willie has no luck at games. Just the other day he was playing Bingo with his friends. Willie had all but five spaces covered on his card but still did not win the game. Can you cover all but five spaces on the Bingo card below in such a way that there are not five spaces covered in a row? Willie did. Remember to watch out for the diagonals when you begin covering spaces.

16

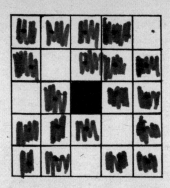

8. AN EXALTATION OF LARKS

Not so long ago we were walking in the woods with a friend. Suddenly I sighted a group of larks clustered on a large bush.

"Look at that flock of larks," I said.

"That is not a flock," our friend informed us. "That is an exaltation of larks."

When we got home I checked and our friend was correct. That set us to thinking about other words which mean a number of one kind of animal. The puzzle below is the result of our work.

Each clue matches a numbered set of squares in the puzzle. Your task is to decide what word means a group of animals named in the clue. That word, if it is correct, will fill the squares and interlock with the words which cross it.

Read the animal name in the clue. Try to decide on the word which means a group of that animal. Check the list following the clues. All the answers are listed there, so you can't miss. Or can you? We hope not.

Don't be too surprised if the word we use is a new one for you. The whole idea of this puzzle

17

is to give you some new words to use. Also, several animals have more than one word to describe a group. We have used one or two of these to keep you on your toes.

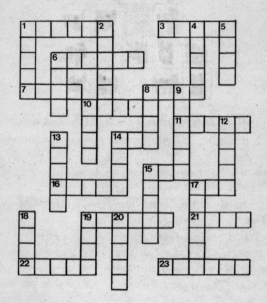

ACROSS

1. Fish
3. Nightingales
6. Chicks
7. Pheasants
8. Bees
10. Sheep
11. Greyhounds
14. Clams
15. Hounds
16. Gnats
17. Whales
19. Peacocks
21. Elk
22. Lions
23. Bears

DOWN

1. Geese	12. Bees
2. Pigs	13. Ducks
4. Goats	14. Gorillas
5. Hares	15. Quail
6. Hawks	17. Geese
8. Elephants	18. Leopards
9. Birds	19. Hounds
10. Hares	20. Foxes

Answers from which to choose:

band	gaggle	nest
bed	gam	pride
brace	gang	school
cast	herd	skein
cloud	hive	skulk
clutch	husk	sleuth
covey	leap	swarm
cry	leash	tribe
down	litter	volery
drove	muster	watch
	mute	

9. ONLY FOR THOSE WITH SHARP EYES

Below is a jumble of letters. Give yourself exactly three minutes to study these letters. At the end of that time write only those letters of the alphabet which do *not* appear in the jumble. Remember now, only three minutes. Ready, set, begin.

```
        A S D F J K L H G A
       R T U F G H E I N O T C
       F C E I U N B T O R
         C M Z R O I U V
           V E R N M I
          T R Y U X E
         S O V N E B T K
       F C O I W Z E N A L
      O W B K L Y X V Z P D A
       G R B N O T I F A U
```

10. THAT'S ENGLISH

As a result of the American Revolution many differences developed in the American and English ways of living. Since America is so far from England certain changes would have come about anyway, but the Revolution speeded things up.

One of those differences was in language. Both nations speak English, but American English is a bit different from English English.

In order to check your ability to understand both these English languages try matching the American words at left with the English words

20

of the same meaning at the right. Each word has a mate with like meaning and each word is used one time only.

American English	English English
1. gas	2 flat
2. apartment	6 lorries
3. diapers	10 porter
4. dessert	9 chips
5. elevator	1 petrol
6. trucks	20 ladders
7. drugstore	22 bonnet
8. television	16 serviette
9. French fries	3 nappies
10. garbageman	7 chemist's
11. runs in nylons	5 lift
12. janitor	4 sweets
13. radio	8 telly
14. car hood	17 underground
15. car trunk	11 queue
16. napkin	23 flannel
17. subway	21 minced beef
18. refrigerator	14 cot
19. to telephone	25 post
20. line of people	24 hoover
21. hamburger	19 ring up
22. crib	18 dustman
23. washcloth	15 fridge
24. vacuum	13 boot
25. mail a letter	12 wireless

21

11. CAN YOU COUNT?

It is surprising how few people can count. Take the figure below, for example. It contains a number of squares. Some squares are small, some a bit larger, and some still larger, but they are squares nevertheless.

Keep in mind that a square must have four sides of equal length and four square corners. Now look at the figure below and count the number of squares it contains.

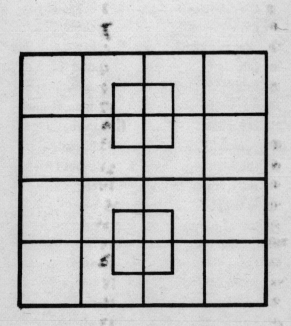

12. LIFE IS A RIDDLE

Life can be a riddle and the riddles which follow certainly prove this to be true. How many of these old favorites do you know?

1. What criminals are strongest?
2. What do you and I do at the same time every day no matter where we are?
3. What makes more noise than a boy practicing his trumpet?
4. What is the difference between a mountain and a spoonful of castor oil?
5. What has only one foot?
6. What did the wood say to the fireplace?
7. Why did the coach kick Cinderella off the team?
8. What happens to food when people overeat?
9. Why did the convict want to play baseball?
10. With which hand is it correct to stir coffee at a formal dinner?
11. What channel can't you get on your TV set?
12. Why was it better to be a history student in Colonial days than it is now?
13. What did one light bulb say to another light bulb?
14. What did the envelope say when the secretary licked it?
15. How are a leaky faucet and a coward alike?
16. What coat is always put on when it is wet?
17. What did one eye say to the other eye?
18. What is another name for a cowardly skin diver?
19. What three letters stand for hard water?

20. What is a smart duck?
21. How are a bad boy and the letter "d" alike?
22. What does Robin do when he gets up in the morning?
23. What did the boy's mother do when he swallowed her pen?
24. What was the little cannibal who ate his father and mother?
25. What was the cannibal who ate his father's sister?

13. MUSIC MAKERS

Whether you play an instrument or not you should not find this puzzle too difficult. Just let the clue guide you and fill in the spaces provided.

1. _ L _ _ _
2. _ _ E _ _ _   _ _ _ _
3. T _ _ _
4. _ _ S _ _ _ _
5. _ _ _ M _ _ _
6. _ _ A _ _ _ _ _
7. K _ _ _ _ _ _ _ _ _
8. _ _ _ E
9. _ _ _ M _ _ _ _
10. _ _ _ _   _ _ U _
11. S _ _ _ _ _ _ _ _
12. _ I _ _ _ _
13. C _ _ _ _ _ _

24

1. Close relative of the piccolo
2. This was originally a hunting horn in France.
3. Largest of the brass instruments
4. The "clown" of the orchestra
5. Early relatives of this instrument gave battle commands thousands of years ago.
6. Very common woodwind
7. Also called the tympani
8. Looks much like a clarinet but uses a double reed
9. The word "slide" is often used as part of this instrument's name.
10. This big fellow is a timekeeper.
11. A reed instrument made of brass
12. Most common stringed instrument
13. Would you believe in a bronze percussion instrument?

14. LETTER MAZES

A Letter Maze is a collection of hidden words. Each word is spelled correctly. Some go across the page, others are written up and down, and a few are written diagonally. Some are spelled backwards and many overlap one another. How many of the hidden words in each maze can you find? It is a good idea to circle the answers as you locate them in order to keep track of your progress.

I. West of the Mississippi

This maze contains the names of the twenty-four states west of the Mississippi River. An atlas may help you if your memory is poor.

```
A N A T N O M K A N S A S T
L E A I N R O F I L A C A A
A V H I R U O S S I M R S N
S A N A T O S E N N I M N O
K D O W H O A N O Z I R A T
A A R A V N X I C G A N K G
N F T H O R E G O N M E R N
A U H I O N T H L I O W A I
I C D A L I A U O M H M T H
S T A T E D G I R O A E E S
I F K I I N O S A Y L X X A
U M O H O W X A D W K I C W
O O T O A R N I O A O C O L
L Y A T O K A D H T U O S O
A W A K S A R B E N O R T U
```

II. Major U.S. Cities

According to the 1971 *World Almanac* there were twenty-five cities in the United States which had populations of over 500,000 people in the 1970 census. The names of these cities are in the following maze. Can you find them all? If you get stuck turn to the answer section for those city names you don't know. Then circle them in the maze.

```
S A N F R A N C I S C O O C P
U A I H P L E D A L I H P D I
B A L T I M O R E V N E D N T
M N X L S A N A N T O N I O T
U E I O A S A N S I U O L T S
L W N S D D T I O R T E D G B
O O E A E A H T B O S T O N U
C R O N T P H O U S T O N I R
H L H G M I L W A U K E E H G
I E P E C L E V E L A N D S H
C A M L N E W O G E I D N A S
A N N E W Y O R K O N A S W K
G S G S I L O P A N A I D N I
O R E L L I V N O S K C A J E
S A T S E A T T L E R A G N T
```

III. United States Presidents

The names of thirty-six Americans who have served as President are hidden in the maze below. Grover Cleveland is listed only one time though he often is included twice in lists of Presidents. Four names must be located twice in the maze. These names are Adams, Johnson, Harrison, and Roosevelt. When you run out of Presidential names take a quick peek at the answers for those you forgot, then find and circle them in the maze.

```
W A S H I N G T O N O X I N B
A D A M S E Y A H O O V E R U
H A R D I N G R A S O E R O C
A M O N R O E K T N X I O O H
R S A R T H U R L H R S M S A
R M C K I N L E Y O U E L E N
I E C R E I P L L J P N L V A
S K E N N E D Y H O O H I E N
O S F A T F A T O S L O F L D
N A M U R T X I N H L W D T N
N O S I R R A H R I I E L N A
T L E V E S O O R L N R E O L
T N A R G J A O S O C K I S E
J E F F E R S O N F O E F K V
M A D I S O N V U F L N R C E
G A R V A N B U R E N S A A L
R O O E G D I L O O C R G J C
```

28

15. BEGINNER'S NUMBER CROSS

Below are a number of three-place numbers. The object of this puzzle (and the one following) is to place each of these numbers in the puzzle so all numbers interlock with one another. Use each number only one time. It is a good idea to check off numbers as they are used. Plan ahead and write lightly are the only suggestions you should need.

The numbers given are in their correct places, so you can check them off the list right away.

146	301	521	740
158	457	537	791
276	462	558	823
278	491	639	826
284	503	672	914

16. NUMBER CROSS

Each number below has a definite place in the number puzzle. The digits in the puzzle are placed correctly. Just interlock the numbers around the digits given and keep placing numbers correctly to solve the puzzle.

12345	23514	34152	45132
12435	24351	34215	45231
12453	24513	34251	51243
14253	25314	35124	51324
15234	31425	41325	51342
15324	31452	41523	51432
21435	31524	43251	53142
23415	34125	43521	54312

17. SHORTIES FOR SHARPIES

Twenty-five shorties follow. None of them should take any length of time to answer, though a few are a bit on the tricky side. Be sure you have read each shorty carefully before answering it. Now get to it.

1. July and August are two consecutive months with thirty-one days each. What other two consecutive months have thirty-one days each?
2. What is the opposite of not good?
3. Two boys played four games of checkers. Each boy won three games. How can this be?
4. What is a philatelist?
5. Two mothers and two daughters went for lunch. The meal for each cost $1.10. The total price for all the meals came to $3.30. How did this happen?
6. If three cats can catch three rats in three minutes, how long will it take one hundred cats to catch one hundred rats?
7. A fisherman caught a fish which weighed twenty pounds plus half its weight. What did it weigh?
8. If you went to sleep at eight o'clock at night and set the alarm for nine the following morning, how much sleep would you get?
9. How do you pronounce Kentucky's capital? Is it Louisville or Louieville?
10. Divide forty by one half and add ten to your answer.
11. A woman voted for mayor in a town elec-

31

tion. She is the mayor's sister, but the mayor is not her brother. How come?

12. Some months have thirty days and some have thirty-one. How many have twenty-eight in them?

13. The Equator is about 25,000 miles in length. What is the size of the North Pole?

14. A freezing hunter had only one match left when he found a cabin. In the cabin were a kerosene lantern, a wood-burning stove, and a fireplace. Which should he light first?

15. A man is cutting wood for his fireplace. Each cut he makes takes him two minutes. How long will it take him to cut a ten-foot log into two-foot-long chunks for his fireplace?

16. Why can't a man living in Boston be buried in Hawaii?

17. Which is larger — half a dozen dozen or six-dozen dozen?

18. A line of cars just went past our house. There were three cars in front of one car and three cars behind another car. How many cars went past in that line?

19. What number divided by four is the same as that number minus four? (Be careful, now!)

20. What number is as much larger than twenty-six as it is smaller than eighty-four?

21. The name of what musical instrument contains four letters, three of which are vowels?

22. What states have the same situation as that found in the above question?

23. A farmer had four haystacks in one field

and nine in another. If he combined them, how many stacks would he have?

24. What word is usually pronounced incorrectly?

25. Who wrote the best-known autobiography of Benjamin Franklin?

18. STARS IN YOUR EYES

Unless you are very lucky or especially good at math puzzles this magic star may cause you to see stars. Use the even numbers from 2 through 24 for this puzzle. Place one number in each circle and use each number one time only. When the numbers are correctly placed each line of four numbers will total 52. Your magic star will have six lines of four numbers and each line will add to 52. Remember now, use each number only once and use only the even numbers from 2 through 24.

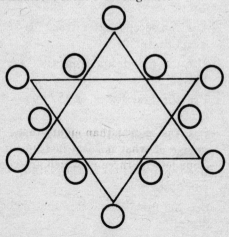

19. STATE NICKNAMES

Here is a chance to show off your knowledge of state nicknames. At the left of the page is a column of blanks to be filled one at a time. To the right of each blank is a direction telling you which state to use and what letter from that state's name to place in the blank. Each clue uses the state's nickname. All you need to do is match a state name with the nickname and fill in the blank. Simple, isn't it.

1. ____ Use the first letter in the name of the "Golden State."

2. ____ Use the second letter in the name of the "Silver State."

3. ____ Use the first letter in the name of the "Cornhusker State."

4. ____ Use the first letter from the "Lone Star State."

5. ____ Use the second letter from the "Bluegrass State."

6. ____ Use the first letter from the "Empire State."

7. ____ Use the first letter of the "Tar Heel State."

8. ____ Use the first letter of the "Hoosier State."

9. ____ Use the first letter in the "Grand Canyon State."

10. ____ Use the first letter from the "Pelican State."

11. ___ Use the first letter of the "Palmetto State."

12. ___ Use the first letter of the "Volunteer State."

13. ___ Use the first letter of the "Land of the Midnight Sun."

14. ___ Use the last letter of the "Green Mountain State."

15. ___ Use the second letter in the "Garden State."

The column of letters above should now spell the nickname for Colorado, the authors' home state.

20. MISSING MATH

Working math problems may not be your favorite sport, but you should enjoy solving the half dozen which follow. Most of the work is already done. All you need to do is fill in the missing numbers, marked with ___'s. Think a little bit and this is pretty easy. Remember to check your work.

```
1.      _  4  6      2.       _  3  0  _  4
        5  _  8               -  _  6  5  _
     +  4  9  _                4  _  5  3
     _____
        _  3  5  6
```

3.   __   2   __   4   4.   2   1   __   __

        ×   __   3)6 __ __ __

     __ __   7   0   __

                        __

                     1   8

                     __ __

                        __

                        6

5.   __   0   4   __   6.   3   __   __

       ×   __   3   ×   __   5   __

     __   7   __ __ __   1   2   __ __

   1 __ __ __ __   5

   __ __ __ __ __   8   __ __ __   5

                   2   2   __   9   7   __

21. DOG SHOW

Everything was going fine at the dog show until someone thoughtlessly blew a training whistle. Dogs from the entire show answered and the place was a mess. Everything is straightened out now except for a few signs. Would you help the show officials repair the damaged signs? Just match the part at the left with the part at the right and the sign will be as good

36

as new. If words repeat on either side it means they are to be used for more than one sign.

1. Saint	Retriever
2. Great	Husky
3. Norwegian	Pyrenees
4. Irish	Corgi
5. Scottish	Setter
6. Labrador	Sheep Dog
7. Brittany	Terrier
8. Cocker	Bernard
9. Boston	Terrier
10. Bull	Spaniel
11. Doberman	Retriever
12. German	Dane
13. Siberian	Shepherd
14. Irish	Mastiff
15. Golden	Terrier
16. Rhodesian	Spaniel
17. Welsh	Wolfhound
18. Old English	Pinscher
19. Fox	Elkhound
20. Great	Ridgeback

22. TONGUE TWISTERS

Hard-to-say tongue twisters have been around for longer than anyone can remember. Try your skill on these old favorites by reading each one aloud rapidly three times. Can you get through them three times in a row without trouble? Bet not.

1. A big blue bug bit a big black bear,
   Made a big black bear bleed blood.

2. She sells seashells by the seashore.

3. A fly and a flea flew up a flue.
   "Let us fly!" said the flea.
   "Let us flee!" said the fly.
   So they flew through a flaw in the flue.

4. Susan shines shoes and socks;
   Socks and shoes shines Susan.
   She ceased shining shoes and socks,
   For shoes and socks shock Susan.

5. Suddenly swerving, seven small swans
   swam silently southward.

6. Silly Sally swiftly shooed seven silly sheep.

7. Three gray geese in a green field grazing.

8. Old oily Ollie oils old oily autos.

9. The old school scold sold the school coal scuttle.

10. The suitor wore shorts and a short shooting suit to a short shoot.

23. MATHEMAGIC

Not all magic is performed by magicians on the stage. The mathemagic problems which follow should prove to you that the authors are able to perform magic for you. Do each problem being sure to follow the instructions exactly. Then turn to the answer section. You will find that we always predict your answer. If your answer does not agree with ours, go back and check your work. Remember, we're magic so our answers can't be wrong.

I

1. Write the last four digits in your phone number.
2. Multiply by two.
3. Add five.
4. Multiply by fifty.
5. Add your age.
6. Add the number of days in an ordinary year.
7. Subtract 615.
8. See our answer.

II

1. Write a number.
2. Multiply by two.
3. Add fifteen.
4. Subtract three.
5. Divide by two.
6. Take away the number you started with.
7. See the answer section.

III

1. Pick a number larger than one hundred.
2. Multiply by two.
3. Add two.
4. Multiply by five.
5. Add twenty-two.
6. Multiply by ten.
7. Take away 320.
8. Cross off the final two digits in your answer.
9. See our prediction.

IV

1. Write a number.
2. Write the next four consecutive numbers.
3. Add the five numbers you now have.
4. Divide the total by five.
5. Subtract two.
6. See our answer.

V

1. List your age.
2. Multiply by two.
3. Take away three.
4. Multiply by fifty.
5. Add fifty-four.
6. Add a number between fifty and ninety.
7. Add ninety-six.
8. See our prediction.

VI

1. Write the number of years of school you have completed.
2. Multiply by four.
3. Add an even number less than one hundred.
4. Divide by two.
5. Subtract half of the number you added in step three.
6. Divide the remainder by two.
7. Check our answer.

VII

1. Choose a number.
2. Multiply it by six.
3. Add twelve.
4. Divide by three.
5. Subtract two.
6. Divide by two.
7. Subtract the beginning number.
8. Check with us.

VIII

1. Write your house number.
2. Double it.
3. Add five.
4. Multiply by fifty.
5. Add your age.
6. Add the days in a leap year.
7. Subtract 616.
8. See our answer.

IX

1. Pick a number.

2. Add two.

3. Multiply by three.

4. Take four away.

5. Multiply by three.

6. Add the number with which you started.

7. Cross out the final number in your answer.

8. See our answer.

X

1. Begin with a number between one and six.

2. Multiply it by five.

3. Add eight.

4. Double your answer.

5. Add another number between one and six.

6. Take away sixteen.

7. Check with us.

24. CAPITAL CROSS-UP

We have used the names of two-dozen state capitals to build the puzzle below. Each block in the puzzle needs to be filled with a letter, of course. In order to help you we have listed the names of the states whose capitals are used. To make the job even easier these states are listed as either "across" or "down." What could be easier! As a final help, Delaware's capital fits in the five spaces going down in the upper left-hand corner. The rest is up to you.

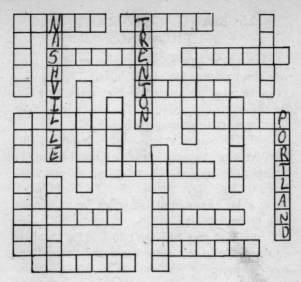

Here are the states whose capitals you need.

ACROSS	DOWN
Arizona	Alaska
Colorado	Delaware
Georgia	Hawaii
Kansas	Idaho
Maine	Maryland
Minnesota	Michigan
Nebraska	Montana
New Hampshire	New Jersey
New Mexico	North Dakota
North Carolina	Oregon
Texas	South Dakota
Wisconsin	Tennessee

43

25. MAGIC SUBTRACTION TRIANGLE

This magic figure uses all the numbers from one through nine for each solution. The object is to place these nine numbers beside the nine dots on the figure. In order for the figure to be magic, however, the numbers have to be carefully placed. The sum of the two side numbers is subtracted from the sum of the two numbers at the points. This is done on all three sides of the triangle. The same answer must be found on all three sides of the figure in order for your solution to be correct.

Remember you add the two middle numbers and subtract their total from the sum of the two end numbers. The answer must be the same for all three sides of the triangle.

Solve this magic subtraction triangle for an answer of 0 all the way around. Then solve it for 3, and finally for 9. Don't be too willing to peek at the answer. It can be done if you will just stay with it.

Don't forget to use the numbers 1 through 9 in every triangle. No number may be repeated nor left out of any solution.

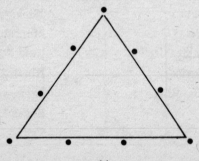

44

26. YOU'VE GOT TO BE KIDDING!

In order to complete the magic square below you may use the *even* numbers from 2 through 32. Each of these even numbers may be used to fill one box. Once a number is used it may not be used again. When the numbers are correctly placed any row, column, or diagonal of four numbers will add to a total of 68. Two numbers are in their correct spaces to give you a start. Naturally these numbers can't be used again.

2			
			32

27. CODES FOR CODEBREAKERS

Codes have been used for years as a means of sending secret messages. Codebreakers have existed for as many years attempting to break codes used for such messages.

Below are five coded statements made by famous Americans. It is your job to break the five codes, all of which are different, and read the statements.

Begin by substituting the letter given as a clue. Place it in all the words in which it appears. Then work on the short words of one or two letters. Move from there to the longer words. Whenever you are sure of a letter, substitute it in all the places it appears in the coded message.

Keep in mind that the codes are different in all five items. The clue given should get you going nicely. Just don't give up too easily. You can break the codes if you work at it.

1. J POMZ SFHSFU UIBU J IBWF CVU POF MJGF UP MPTF GPS NZ DPVOUSZ.

                                   OBUIBO IBMF

F in this code stands for e in the original.

2. ABCBD EBFCB GIFG GHEE GJKJDDJL LIHMI NJO MFA PJ GJPFN.

                                   QBARFKHA SDFATEHA

F here represents a.

3. Z AYBXC WDEDWCW ZVZDFXU DUXCGT HZFFYU XUZFW

                                   ZSIZAZR GDFHYGF

F stands for n.

46

4. HTASA OR RINT E HTOCM ER E GEC
   PAOCM HUU BSUIW HU LOMTH.

   DUUWSUD DOFRUC

   Here A represents e.

5. EJB GKFZ EJLKP HB JCOB EG ABCD LI
   ABCD LEIBFA.

   ADCKNFLK MBFCKG DGGIBOBFE

   B is e.

28. ALPHABETICS

The five puzzles which follow are known as
Alphabetics. An Alphabetic is a small cross-
word puzzle with a big difference. It takes only
twenty-six letters to solve the puzzle. Each puzzle uses each and every letter of the alphabet
to complete the puzzle. Just follow the clues
and be sure the answers you choose fit into the
puzzle spaces correctly. As a hint one letter has
been placed correctly in each puzzle.

I

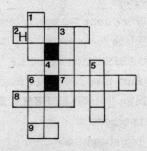

1. Down: Cardboard container
2. Across: Stay in the air near one place (Heli-
   copters do it.)

47

3. Down: Country famous for its pyramids
4. Across: Possessive form of I
5. Down: Short test
6. Down: When the sun rises
7. Across: Pull out
8. Across: Rapid
9. Across: Abbreviation for New Jersey

II

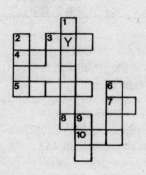

1. Down: Fireplug
2. Down: Work done for pay (plural)
3. Across: Place for exercise
4. Across: Abbreviation for ounce
5. Across: American Indian woman
6. Down: Take fruit from a tree
7. Across: In case of
8. Across: Television
9. Down: Annoy
10. Across: Large relative of the deer

III

1. Down: A kindness
2. Across: Poke
3. Down: A high, whistling sound
4. Across: Poisonous
5. Across: Cheat
6. Down: Dried, they become prunes
7. Down: To chop with an ax
8. Across: His wife is a duchess
9. Across: Abbreviation for square

IV

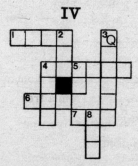

1. Across: Fast, lively dances
2. Down: Air above the earth

49

3. **Down:** A bright, glassy mineral

4. **Across:** A brass percussion instrument

4. **Down:** Cook

5. **Down:** Military policeman

6. **Across:** Bother

7. **Across:** Abbreviation for dozen

8. **Down:** Possess

V

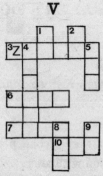

1. **Down:** Abbreviation for vice-president

2. **Down:** Beside

3. **Across:** A gentle breeze

4. **Down:** An igloo builder

5. **Down:** Floor covering

6. **Across:** Cause bad luck

7. **Across:** Wild member of the dog family

8. **Down:** A style which is popular for a time

9. **Down:** Abbreviation for quart

10. **Across:** A deed

Now that you have worked our Alphabetics why not make some of your own. Building your own puzzles is at least as much fun as working ours. Just remember to use every letter of the alphabet one time in making your Alphabetic. Also keep in mind that an Alphabetic may use only twenty-six letters for the entire puzzle. Happy puzzle building!

29. BAKER'S DOZEN

As you know, a baker's dozen equals thirteen. It is said the term comes from the fact that bakers once gave thirteen rolls for a dozen to be sure they didn't miscount and short the buyer. Their action was prompted, it is said, by a royal decree imposing the death penalty on those who cheated their customers. All of which brings us to the fact the thirteen problems which follow should give you a run for your money without cheating you.

1. A band director planned a marching demonstration for his five-dozen band members. During the performance the players marched in two lines, then three, next four, and finally five lines. The night of the performance not all the musicians were present. When the band lined up in two lines, one line was shorter than the other by one player. The same thing happened when the band formed three, then four, and lastly five lines. Each formation found one line short by a player. How many players were absent?

2. Bob and John were playing marbles when Bob said, "If I were to give you one of my marbles we would have the same number."

Replied John, "But if I gave you one of mine you would have twice as many as I."

How many marbles have Bob and John?

3. Hilda likes to have things orderly, especially her cupboards. When she stacks her plates in two piles, one pile has an extra plate. The same thing happens when she tries three and four stacks. Five piles come out even, however, so Hilda always stacks her plates in five equal piles. How many plates has Hilda?

4. Larry is twenty-four years of age and is twice as old as Charles was when Larry was as old as Charles is now. How old is Charles now?

5. A paperboy collected five dollars in coins the other day. The coins were half-dollars, dimes, and pennies. How many of each did he have if he had a total of one hundred coins?

6. Fred discovered that should he subtract seven years from his age and multiply his answer by seven he got the same product as he did when subtracting five years from his age and multiplying the difference by five. How old is Fred?

7. Here is a series of numbers. Read the numbers quickly, writing the next higher number after each is read. Fifty-one, ninety-four, one hundred six, three hundred twenty-seven,

seven hundred sixteen, one thousand eight hundred forty-two, two thousand six hundred seventy-two, four thousand ninety-nine. Now check your answers!

8. While you have your pencil out write the words which mean the following.

A funny story or funny saying
People (or parents)
A common soft drink
The white of an egg

9. Joe's chickens plus five of Lloyd's would make their flocks equal. Lloyd's plus five of Joe's would give Lloyd a flock twice the size of Joe's. How many chickens has each?

10. Bob and Mary are brother and sister. The sum of their ages is eleven. Bob is ten years older than Mary. What are their ages?

11. Can you divide sixty-one into four parts so the first part divided by four equals the second number plus seven, which is the same as the third number times five, and equals the fourth number minus six?

12. Now try dividing seventy-two into four numbers so that the first times two equals the second plus two, which is the same as the third minus two, and is equal to the fourth divided by two.

13. Why did the farmer build his pig pen exactly eight feet wide, sixteen feet long, and four feet high?

53

30. HOW ABOUT THAT!

Sometimes numbers can be made to do the strangest things. Here is a quick test of your ability to make numbers do your bidding. You may write the numbers in any way you wish. You may use any mathematics symbols you wish in writing them. However, you may use only the numbers given in writing your answer.

1. Can you write four 9's so they equal 100?
2. Now try writing six 9's in such a way that they equal 100.
3. Can you make three 3's equal 4?
4. How about making three 3's equal 3?
5. Can two 1's equal 1?
6. Now make six 1's equal 12.
7. Do three 5's equal 6?
8. How about making three 8's equal 0?

The next four are only for experts. Tackle them with care. They may be frustrating.

9. Three 7's can equal 20.
10. Six 3's sometimes equal 100.
11. Eight 4's will equal 500 if you know how.
12. Five 10's also equal 1, but only for a few people.

31. COWBOY WORDS

How is your cowboy talk? You will soon find out. Each of the cowboy words in the list below right matches one of the meanings on the left. How many can you correctly match? A top hand will match them all. A good range hand will get at least twenty correct. A fair cowpoke will answer at least fifteen correctly. Only greenhorns and dudes will match a dozen or less.

1.	Pony or small horse	Adios
2.	Hide out	Arroyo
3.	Cowboy who handles string of horses	Bust
4.	Six-gun	Calaboose
5.	Steal horses or cattle	Cayuse
6.	Good-bye	Chuck
7.	Lynching	Critter
8.	Jail	Dogie
9.	Food	Equalizer
10.	Rawhide rope	Frijoles
11.	Man	Hole up
12.	Wild horse	Hombre
13.	Count	Hoss
14.	Stream or gully	Lariat
15.	Break or gentle a horse	Lope
16.	Cowboy	Mustang
17.	A cow (or any animal)	Necktie Party
18.	String of horses	Puncher
19.	A calf without a mother	Reata
20.	Rope	Remuda
21.	Beans	Rodeo
22.	Hat	Rustle
23.	Horse	Sombrero
24.	A slow gallop	Tally
25.	Contest of Western or cowboy events	Wrangler

32. QUICK NOW!

Give yourself just a few minutes for this little puzzle. All answers are words of three letters. After you've done this one try constructing one of your own. You'll enjoy the project.

ACROSS

1. Consume food
3. Evil
5. Mineral-bearing rock
6. Propel a boat
8. Member of canine family
10. Painting and sculpture
12. Sick
14. Possess
15. Weed chopper
16. Sign of sleepiness

DOWN

1. Found in a cornfield
2. Pull
3. Place of rest
4. Understand (slang)
7. Used in #6 across
9. Petroleum
10. Left after burning
11. Small relative of a foot
12. Lodging place
13. Cover

56

33. DIAMOND IN THE ROUGH

Here is your chance to have a diamond all your own. Just follow the clues below each diamond and you'll be able to build a pretty nice looking diamond. A letter starts the diamond for you. The next step uses that letter and one more to form a word. Each step adds one more letter until the center of the diamond is reached. Then each step takes one letter away until the ending letter is reached. The letters may be used in any order in any step. Just keep adding one letter at a time to build, and take away one letter for each step when narrowing your diamond.

I

e

1. __ __

2. __ __ __

3. __ __ __ __

4. __ __ __ __ __

5. __ __ __ __

6. __ __ __

7. __ __

e

1. Related to been
2. A place of rest
3. Put a curve in
4. Mix together
5. Loan
6. Finish
7. A prefix meaning in

57

II

1. Preposition showing location   a
2. Feline   1. __ __
3. Outer garment   2. __ __ __
4. Seashore   3. __ __ __ __
5. Price   4. __ __ __ __ __
6. Folding bed   5. __ __ __ __
7. Preposition meaning toward   6. __ __ __

     7. __ __

     o

III

1. Pronoun   i
2. Be seated   1. __ __
3. Place   2. __ __ __
4. Steps to cross a fence   3. __ __ __ __
5. Smother   4. __ __ __ __ __
6. Records   5. __ __ __ __ __ __
7. Being alive   6. __ __ __ __ __
8. Fee, ___, foe, fum   7. __ __ __ __
9. In case of   8. __ __ __

     9. __ __

     i

58

IV

1. Masculine pronoun
2. Feminine pronoun
3. Small building
4. Cast by trees
5. Part of the body
6. Past tense of have
7. Put in papers

e
1. __ __
2. __ __ __
3. __ __ __ __
4. __ __ __ __ __
5. __ __ __ __
6. __ __ __
7. __ __
a

V

1. Article
2. Used for cooking
3. Done by hot dog
4. Article of clothing
5. Found in gardens
6. At an angle
7. Final
8. Was seated
9. May mean like

a
1. __ __
2. __ __ __
3. __ __ __ __
4. __ __ __ __ __
5. __ __ __ __ __ __
6. __ __ __ __ __
7. __ __ __ __
8. __ __ __
9. __ __
a

59

VI

a

1. — —
2. — — —
3. — — — —
4. — — — — —
5. — — — — —
6. — — — — —
7. — — — —
8. — — — —
9. — —

e

1. Form of to be
2. Damage or scratch
3. Stuff
4. Rich part of whole milk
5. Shrill cry
6. Packages of paper (one contains 500 sheets)
7. Place where two pieces of cloth are joined
8. The ocean
9. Plural ending

60

VII

a

1. __ __
2. __ __ __
3. __ __ __ __
4. __ __ __ __
5. __ __ __ __ __
6. __ __ __ __ __
7. __ __ __ __ __
8. __ __ __ __
9. __ __ __ __
10. __ __ __
11. __ __

e

1. Abbreviation for agriculture
2. Slang for gun
3. Place to go through a fence
4. Most important part of a theater
5. Metal racks in fireplace for wood to rest on
6. Odd
7. Kitchen stoves
8. Displeasure
9. Fury
10. Form of to be
11. Prefix meaning to do again

61

VIII

a

1. __ __
2. __ __ __
3. __ __ __ __
4. __ __ __ __ __
5. __ __ __ __ __ __
6. __ __ __ __ __ __ __
7. __ __ __ __ __ __ __ __
8. __ __ __ __ __ __ __
9. __ __ __ __ __ __
10. __ __ __ __ __ __
11. __ __ __ __ __
12. __ __ __ __
13. __ __

a

1. Musical syllable
2. Beverage
3. Strong wind
4. A spiritual being
5. Ancient tribe in England
6. Mix-ups
7. Choke
8. Uncommon
9. Land given by the government (as in the old Southwest)
10. Prefix meaning over or across
11. Talk long and excitedly — __ and rave

62

12. Rodent

13. Egyptian sun god

34. DOUBLE TROUBLE

A surprising number of common words contain double letters (such as common in this sentence). Quite a few of these are six-letter words in which the double letters appear in the middle of the word. We've filled in the double letters and supplied a clue to help you complete the double trouble words below. A few may be a bit misleading but don't let them stump you.

I

— — b b — —   Hare

— — b b — —   Mob

— — b b — —   Overshoe

— — b b — —   Broken building

— — b b — —   Hair holder

— — b b — —   Thief

II

— — g g — —   Silly laugh

— — g g — —   Move quickly back and forth

— — g g — —   Eye protector

— — g g — —   Argue

— — g g — —   Lumberjack

— — g g — —   Fly larva

63

III

_ _ 11 _ _	Go after
_ _ 11 _ _	Roar
_ _ 11 _ _	Slice of boneless fish
_ _ 11 _ _	Needs powder to be of use
_ _ 11 _ _	A fish
_ _ 11 _ _	Young hen

IV

_ _ s s _ _	Top of corn plant
_ _ s s _ _	Ship
_ _ s s _ _	Long-eared dog
_ _ s s _ _	Learning experience
_ _ s s _ _	Item preserved from the past
_ _ s s _ _	Oyster's cousin

V

_ _ t t _ _	Baby's plaything
_ _ t t _ _	To decide
_ _ t t _ _	Tell on
_ _ t t _ _	Okay for sailors, perhaps
_ _ t t _ _	Big fight
_ _ t t _ _	Not quite best

VI

_ _ z z _ _	Gun's mouth
_ _ z z _ _	Bewilder
_ _ z z _ _	Fail
_ _ z z _ _	Sound of frying meat

___ ___ z z ___ ___   Drink too much too fast

___ ___ z z ___ ___   Confuse by bright lights

35. MIND BINDERS

The problems which follow have been called Mind Binders for a good reason. They are more than likely to place your mind in a bit of a bind. In any case, don't be too quick to give up and look at the answer. Give yourself a chance to solve the problem and come up with a correct answer before giving in. Don't let a little puzzle whip you!

I. Scrambled Occupations

Three men, Joe, Dick, and Bob, are engaged in two occupations each. Their occupations are storekeeper, musician, painter, butler, barber, and gardener. From the following facts decide which two occupations are carried on by each man.

1. The painter bought a quart of turpentine from the storekeeper.

2. The butler made the musician angry by laughing at his mustache.

3. The butler dated the painter's sister.

4. Both the musician and the gardener like to go hunting with Joe.

5. Bob beat both Dick and the painter at chess.

6. Dick owed the gardener half a dollar.

65

II. Clever Thieves

A farmer had the finest patch of watermelons in the county. In order to protect them from thieves he dug a ditch ten feet wide and ten feet deep around his rectangular melon patch. He then filled the ditch with water and thought his melons were safe, since it would be very difficult to swim across the ditch with the huge melons.

You can imagine the farmer's surprise when he awoke one morning to discover his melon patch had been raided. The thieves had left behind two heavy planks they had used to cross the ditch. Obviously the two planks had been made into a bridge but the puzzled farmer could not see how. Each plank was exactly nine feet, ten inches long. They had not been nailed or tied together. In fact, the two planks had not been fastened together in any way.

How had the thieves outsmarted the farmer?

III. On the Road to St. Ives

A traveler made up the following rhyme.

As I was going to St. Ives,

I met a man with seven wives.

Each wife had seven children.

Each child had seven cats.

Each cat had seven kittens.

How many were going to St. Ives?

Can you answer the question in the final line of his rhyme?

IV. Busy Bus

Read the following item about the busy bus carefully. When you finish reading it you will be asked to answer a question without looking back over the paragraph.

A bus left the station empty and started on its route. At the first stop it picked up four passengers. At the next stop it picked up three more passengers. Stopping again it let two men off and picked up five women. The next stop found a woman getting off and seven people getting on. Two blocks later the bus stopped again and three men got on. One more stop and five people got off while only one got on.

The question is, how many stops did the bus make in the story?

V. Hunting in the Dark

A hunter arose long before daylight to go duck hunting with three friends. Quickly and quietly he gathered his clothing and slipped out of the bedroom, being careful not to awaken his sleeping wife. When he reached the living room he realized he had forgotten to get a pair of socks to wear. What was worse, he had two colors of socks in the dresser drawer — black and white. In the dark he couldn't tell one from the other. To make matters still worse his socks were not in pairs in the drawer but were tossed in loose.

What is the smallest number of socks the poor hunter needed to pull out of the drawer in order to be sure he had a matching pair?

VI. A Rocky Problem

Larry Bryce had contracted to construct a basement for a new home on a steep hillside. Poor Larry had run into more than his share of problems in the job. To begin with, the hillside was so steep that dirt and rocks kept sliding into the basement as Larry's bulldozer worked. Then after the bulldozer had finished and gone home, the concrete company had called Larry to tell him the concrete would be delivered a day early. Larry had worked most of the night getting the forms ready to pour the concrete when it arrived. Now Larry was looking at what seemed the last straw. A large boulder had rolled down the hillside and was in the middle of the basement. It was too big for Larry and his helper to lift out of the basement. They didn't have time for a crane to be called to come and lift it out. The concrete would arrive in four hours.

"I'm licked," Larry moaned. "There is no way to get that boulder out of the basement in time."

His helper grinned. "If it is worth a raise I'll tell you what we can do."

The helper got his raise and Larry kept his cool. How?

VII. Large Inheritance

A young man inherited a large piece of land from his father. In the old man's will the inheritance was mentioned in detail. The final statement was very important to the young man.

It said: This piece of land is one mile from north to south and one mile from east to west. It is a perfect square. It must remain a perfect square and it must always be one mile from the northern border to the southern, and one mile from the eastern border to the western. If this is changed in any way the land will go to my brother instead of my son.

At the time the will was read this statement did not bother the young man. Several years later it did, though. By that time the value of land in that area had risen greatly.

The young man wanted in the worst way to sell some of the land but knew if he did he would lose the entire inheritance. One day his father's brother came to the young man and suggested the land was becoming so valuable it might be a good idea to sell some of it.

"Sure," said the young man to his uncle. "If I do, then you get it all."

"Not so," replied his uncle. "I'm already well off. That is why my brother gave you all the land instead of dividing it between us. He knew I didn't need money. However, if I show you how to sell half the land and still not violate the terms of the will what would it be worth to you?"

His nephew answered promptly. "I'll split the profits with you."

"It's a deal," said the uncle.

Five minutes later the young man knew how to sell half the land while keeping the borders and shape of the land according to the will. How did he do it?

VIII. Ship and Ladder

A captain anchored his ship and threw a rope ladder over the side. The ladder's steps were one foot apart. The twenty-fourth step was just above the water. During the next six hours the tide rose five and one-half feet. Now which step on the ladder is just above the water?

IX. Drawing Exercise

Below are nine dots. Connect all nine dots using four perfectly straight lines. Do not lift your pencil from the paper until you have drawn the fourth straight line.

X. What a Lot of Handshaking

Eight businessmen got together for lunch. As each man entered the room he shook hands with all the other men present. By the time the eighth and last man was present there had been quite a number of handshakes. Just exactly how many handshakes had there been?

XI. They Are Relatives

A man was walking along a dusty road when he spotted a farmhouse. When he reached the house he asked the farmer for permission to get a drink of cold water from the well. The farmer agreed and said that the young man beside the well would draw the water for the thirsty traveler.

After getting a drink the man stopped to thank the farmer. Then he added, "That fellow at the well looks a lot like you. Are you related?"

The farmer replied, "Brothers and sisters have I none, but that man's father is my father's son."

How were the two related?

XII. Train Travel

A train left Chicago at a speed of sixty miles an hour. At the same instant another train left Boston traveling at a speed of only fifty miles an hour. If both trains keep moving at the same rate of speed at which they started, which will be farther from Boston when the two meet?

XIII. That's a Crazy Way to Measure Water

A science teacher gave Joe two buckets. One held exactly three gallons and the other held five gallons and not a drop more. There were no markings on the buckets for Joe to use in measuring water.

"Now," said the teacher, "I want you to mea-

71

sure out exactly one gallon of water using these two buckets. You may fill and empty the buckets as often as you want. However when a bucket is filled you can't guess at part of a bucket. The only way to know how much water is put into a bucket from the faucet is to fill it completely. After that you may pour from one bucket to the other just so long as you can prove the reason for what you are doing."

"Is that all?" Joe asked.

"No," replied the teacher. "Then do the same for two, three, four, five, six, seven, and eight gallons."

"Is that all?" Joe asked again.

"That's all," the teacher answered. "You have half an hour."

Joe got an A. What would you have gotten? Write your answers out and remember the teacher's instructions. Three, five, and eight are simple. So are the others if you think.

XIV. That's Easy

Write eleven thousand eleven hundred eleven.

XV. What a Question!

There are questions and then there are questions. Many may be answered either yes or no depending upon the circumstances. One question, however, may never be answered with a yes. What is that question?

XVI. That's a Belt?

Kenneth had eaten too well and his waistline was telling the tale. Ken had just purchased a new pair of trousers and another belt. This belt was fifty-four inches long. The belt he had just outgrown had been forty-eight inches long. Kenneth knew he had grown until he was two inches bigger through the middle. If I keep eating until I get as big as the earth, Kenneth thought, I wonder what would happen. If I were as big as the earth and had a belt that fit, then I grew two more inches across the middle, how much longer would my new belt have to be?

We doubt that Ken will actually get that large, but if he does how much bigger would his belt have to be should he then gain two inches through the middle?

XVII. Is There Such a Word?

What three letters can you add to the beginning and to the end of "ergro" to form a common word? The three letters at the beginning are in the same order as at the end.

XVIII. What About This Word?

In the English language there are a few words which contain all the vowels. There are a few, but very few. Perhaps the shortest word in English which contains all five vowels is the name of a tree. What is this word?

XIX. Lunch Date

Three men whose last names were Brown, Green, and Black went out for lunch. The man wearing a green tie said, "We have the same color ties on as our last names, but none of the ties matches the name of the man wearing it."

"That's right," Brown agreed.

Which man wore which tie?

XX. That's an Order!

The following digits are in a logical order. Look them over carefully and decide what that order is. Don't give up until you have discovered this correct order. That is an order!

8, 5, 4, 9, 1, 7, 6, 3, 2, 0

36. DESIGNOGRAMS

As you can see, a Designogram begins with a pattern of letters. To complete the puzzle just follow the clues and fill in the empty spaces. After you complete these Designograms try making some of your own.

I

1. e ___ e
2. e ___ e
3. ___ e e ___
4. ___ e e ___
5. e ___ e
6. e ___ e

1. Comfort, luxury
2. Cutting part of a knife blade
3. Keep an appointment, get together
4. Three equal a yard
5. Edge of a roof (nearly always written as a plural)
6. Other person (someone ___)

II

1. o ___ o
2. F o o D
3. o S L o
4. b o o t
5. o ___ o

1. Atop of
2. Needed to sustain life
3. Norway's capital
4. Kick
5. The "lower priced" spread

75

III

1. a __ __ __ a
2. __ a __ a __
3. __ __ a __ __
4. __ a __ a __
5. a __ __ __ a

1. Place a rodeo is held
2. Man-made waterway
3. Carpenter's tool
4. Island nation in the Pacific
5. Hello or good-bye

IV

1. e __ __ __ e
2. __ e __ e __
3. __ __ e __ __
4. __ e __ e __
5. e __ __ __ e

1. Wear away by wind or water
2. Flat and even
3. Tame a horse
4. High temperature
5. Rub out

V

1. a _ _ _ _ _ _ a
2. a _ _ _ _ _ a
3. a _ _ _ _ a
4. a _ _ a
5. a _ _ _ _ a
6. a _ _ _ _ _ a
7. a _ _ _ _ _ _ a

1. Math which uses unknowns
2. One-celled pond animal
3. Pleasant smell
4. Size of a surface
5. First letter in Greek alphabet
6. Fleet of warships
7. Plant grown for horse and cattle feed

77

VI

1.   __ t __
2.   t __ t
3.   t ___ t
4.   t ____ t
5.   __ t __
6.   __ t __ t __
7.   t ___ t
8.   t _____ t
9.   __ t ___ t __
10.   __ t t __
11.   __ t ___ t __
12.   t _____ t
13.   t _____ t
14.   t _____ t
15.   t _____ t

1. Consumed food
2. Small child
3. School book
4. Wind together, turn around
5. Fire starter
6. California is one
7. Attract
8. One who uses a typewriter
9. Often called "tom walkers," they let one walk high in the air.
10. Reach an agreement
11. Begins
12. Top of a tank (it turns)
13. Wild storm
14. Traitor
15. Wild, upset

37. THE UNHAPPY GROCER

A grocer friend of ours was the happiest fellow alive until just the other day. He had a number of signs with movable letters to use in advertising his fruits and vegetables. A careless worker knocked his signs off the table before the grocer had the letters firmly attached. As a result the letters became badly scrambled. Will you help our unhappy grocer straighten out his signs?

Be sure to use all the letters given in each group in spelling your answers.

1. Three fruits are in this collection of letters.

   a a a c e e e h l p p p p r

2. Here are three vegetables.

   a a c c c h i n n o o p r r r s t

3. Three more vegetables are jumbled here.

   a a c e e e h l p q r s s u y

4. Here are three more vegetables.

   b c c o e e e i l m n n o o r t t u u u

5. Three citrus fruits are in this scramble.

   a e e e g i l l m m n n o o r

6. Three more fruits are here.

   a c c e h i l m o p p r r r t u y

79

7. Now try these three vegetables.

a a i i m n n o o p p p r r s t t t u

8. These three fruits are completely tangled.

a d e e f g i i l o t v

9. These last three fruits are a real mess. Can you untangle them?

a a e e e e f g g i i i m m n n n o p p r r r r s t t u

10. The last three vegetables totally baffled the poor grocer. Can you help him?

a a a a a a a b g g m p r r s s t u u y

38. JUMBLES

A number of related words are spelled correctly in each Jumble. The title tells you what kind of words are hidden in the Jumble and how many to look for. Begin in the upper left-hand corner and draw a line from letter to letter until you spell a word. Then break the line and start another word in a square next to the one on which you stopped. Go on like this until you have spelled the required words and used all the Jumble letters once and once only.

Your line connecting letters may go up and down or across but never diagonally. Each Jumble starts in the upper left-hand corner and ends in the upper right.

I. Ten State Names

Since this is likely to be a bit confusing, we've underlined the first word (Ohio) and the last word (New Mexico) to get you started. Remember, use each letter only once. As a final hint, the state after Ohio is Colorado. See it?

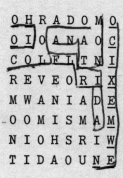

II. Twelve Colors

Remember to begin at the upper left and finish at the upper right. Watch out for violet and crimson. They come right after purple.

```
P I N K Y B L U E
R C T L E Y R G K
I L E L O A E E C
M O I V W R G N A
S O L E P O W N L
O N P R U R H W B
R A N G E B I T E
```

81

III. African Safari — Twelve Animals

The ostrich may give you trouble but the python is coiled right up the right-hand side of the puzzle.

```
L A L O E L E D
I F F U B H P N
O N Z E A A L A
R O G B R N E N
I L O N I T H O
A L N K H R T Y
H M O E C H E P
I O O Y I G F F
P P S T R I R A
```

39. THINKIES

Thinkies are problems for thoughtful people. Each of the Thinkies following has a logical or reasonable answer to the question asked at the end. Some of the answers are pretty obvious. Some are downright hard to pin down.

Read each of the Thinkies carefully and give the question some real thought. Don't give up too easily. You can usually arrive at the answer with just a little thought.

I. Old Friends

Bill Brown was strolling along the main street of his hometown when he met an old school friend whom he hadn't seen in over ten years. As they chatted, Bill and his friend discovered they both had much to catch up on.

Midway in the conversation Bill mentioned he was married and had a daughter.

"What a coincidence," remarked his friend. "I have a daughter, too. In fact, she is just coming out of that store now. I was waiting for her when you happened by."

Bill spoke to the seven-year-old girl when she reached them.

"Hello," he said. "How are you?"

"I'm fine," she answered.

"What's your name?" he asked.

"I'm named after my mother," she replied.

Though neither Bill nor his friend had mentioned the names of their spouses, Bill said immediately, "So you're named Mary, are you."

"Yes," answered the child with a happy smile.

How did Bill know her name?

II. Poor J.C. Richards

J.C. Richards was fast and every sportswriter knew it. Most of the spectators expected him to set a record for the mile today. Conditions were perfect. There was almost no breeze blowing and the sun was not so hot as to be a hindrance.

At the starting line he was in the inside position and ready for a fast start. When the starting signal was given he jumped into an early lead and stayed in front for the entire mile.

The crowd went wild when his winning time was announced. He had set a new world's record. Jubilation turned to sorrow when seconds later it was announced that he had been disqualified due to an infraction of the rules. J.C., however, had not committed the violation. The rules had been broken by another individual, but J.C. was disqualified.

Why?

III. Beloved Librarian

There were many who claimed the Middleton Public Library couldn't operate without Thelma Brown's guiding hand. Though she modestly denied this, she was pleased that members of the community recognized her contributions to the library. Thelma had twice been offered the opportunity to assume leadership of the entire library as head librarian. Both times she had refused, saying she enjoyed running her own department and being able to meet the public and aid them in their search for enjoyment and understanding. During the last five of her twenty-two years at the library, however, Thelma hadn't circulated one book from her department. For that matter she hadn't even handed a patron a book to use in the library. She hadn't so much as helped a customer locate a book.

Why not?

IV. Poor Stella

Stella Wilkins had been a faithful employee of the Newton School District for twenty-eight of her forty-nine years. Everyone viewed her as a permanent fixture at the Newton High School. Teachers, parents, children, and school officials all respected Stella. However, when the school board voted all teachers a $250 raise Stella didn't receive that amount. Instead, her raise was only $200. In spite of the fact that everyone knew Stella's raise was only $200 no one objected.

Why was this so?

V. Border Guard

Willy Snyder had guarded the ugly stone wall which divided Berlin for well over a year now. He grieved to see the city in which he had been raised divided into two separate cities with two different ways of life. It was all because of the horrible Berlin Wall. He could remember when people had been able to visit back and forth between East and West Berlin, but that was past.

On this particular evening Willy was brooding over the future when his sharp eyes noted movement along the Wall. Two men were rapidly cutting away the tangle of barbed wire atop the Wall. Even as Willy watched, two other guards ran toward the escaping men. The guards didn't try to stop them but joined them.

Though Willy did not fire at the men nor raise an alarm, neither did he join the escaping men. Willy's hatred of Communism was well known by his friends and fellow guards. In spite of this, Willy made no move to cross the Wall.

Why?

VI. Overpaid?

Captain Burnell had served the United States for nearly thirty years as a member of the armed forces. He was fond of saying he was just about the oldest captain in the armed services. When he and Bess, his wife, decided he should retire, they set about figuring the income they could expect from his retirement pay. It was with no surprise that he discovered his retirement pay would be more than that of a major with the same number of years in the service.

How could Captain Burnell receive more than a major?

VII. London Smog

Smog had settled on London. It was so dense that public and private transportation had long since stopped running. Public buildings were closed until the thick, wet blanket of smog might lift. The dark, soupy mess in the air covering the city blocked out even the streetlights. London was in total darkness.

An elderly man leaned on his cane in a pub and listened to the conversation around him. His white hair ringed his pale face and his hand trembled slightly. The noisy conversations came to a sudden halt when a newcomer pushed into the pub.

The new arrival was a doctor who was exhausted and frantic. He had been called to an emergency but was quite lost and nearly done in from his frantic search in the blackness for the address to which he had been called.

When the murmur died down following this statement, the elderly gentleman with the cane and white hair asked the address. When he was told the address he realized at once it was in the neighborhood. Without saying more he took the dazed doctor by the arm and led him into the smog-dark night. Within minutes he had guided the doctor to the house in time to treat the emergency victim.

How was the old man able to do this so easily?

VIII. Funny Farm

Farming had always offered long hours and few financial rewards for Clarence Burget. If he wasn't busy harvesting, then he was engaged in planting, getting ready for harvest, repairing his equipment, and the hundred and one time consuming activities which fill the lives of farmers the world over. For years he had sworn he would leave his occupation as a farmer and work in the city. Yet each year he continued his farming operation. It was as a neighbor told him, "It is not as though you had to worry about plowing and rain as do most farmers. Your only real worry is wind at harvest time because you can work even if it is raining. Also, you don't have to pay taxes on a lot of land because you don't have much. Your farming equipment consists of only one piece of power machinery and you don't have to feed a lot of cattle like I do. You have about the best farming setup in the state."

Just what sort of farming operation was the neighbor describing?

IX. A Killer is Loose

When top billing in Seller Brothers Circus was given the high wire act instead of the trapeze act, everyone knew trouble would develop. No one, however, was prepared for the death of the high wire artist during his performance before a crowd of 6,000. Detectives were summoned by the manager when it was discovered the wire had been cut enough to weaken it. The weight of the high wire performer had caused the weakened wire to break.

An immediate search located a pair of wire cutters in the clothing trunk of a member of the trapeze troupe. Under questioning he admitted weakening the wire with the wire cutters so it would break when used during the act.

In spite of his confession the man was not tried for murder nor for manslaughter.

Any idea why not?

X. Wild Ride

Johnny Lewis pressed harder on the accelerator of the Cadillac sending it leaping forward even faster than it had been traveling. The sirens of the two police cars somewhere in back of Johnny's speeding vehicle wailed their warning. Drivers hearing the warning sirens scattered to safety before the three advancing cars. Johnny drove deftly and without fear, though Herry Hendricks beside him sat white-faced and quiet. A glance in the rearview mirror revealed the first of the two police cruisers close behind. The other was still lost in the rear.

The leading police car had pulled to within fifty feet of Johnny's speeding vehicle when

Johnny braked hard and turned sharply into a drive leading to a large building. The officer barely slowed in time to avoid hitting Johnny's Cadillac as it pulled to a halt. When the flushed officer jumped from his car and dashed toward the door from which Johnny was alighting his only comment was, "That was quite a job of driving, fella."

In spite of the fact that Johnny had run over a dozen red lights, exceeded the speed limits, switched traffic lanes too many times to count, and not stopped at the sound of the police sirens, he was not given a ticket.

Why?

40. HIDEOUTS

A common word is hiding out in each sentence below. It may be all or part of two or more words. The example explains:

It is *not ice.*   notice

1. In this job a man ages rapidly.

2. Her injured leg almost healed.

3. Jones is at tackle today.

4. Those fat Herefords are ready for market.

5. A speech by Harold is likely long.

6. Bob's trip east was a success.

7. Scratches mar the furniture.

8. That new tie clip sets off your ties nicely.

9. Don't blame dial phones when you get the wrong number.

10. Our tool and die selection is the largest in the state.

89

41. QUIZ TIME

Feeling sharp? Then it is time for a short quiz or two. The first two quizzes include answers from which to choose. The final three leave you on your own. Happy quizzing.

I. American Presidents

1. Which President of the United States had the most children?
2. Who was our tallest President?
3. What President was shortest?
4. Which President was heaviest?
5. Which President was the youngest when he took office?
6. Who was our only unmarried President?
7. Who was President the shortest time?
8. Which President held office longest?
9. Which President lived the longest?
10. Which President made the shortest inaugural address?

Choose your answers from the following Presidents.

John Adams	Franklin D. Roosevelt
James Buchanan	Theodore Roosevelt
William Henry Harrison	William Howard Taft
Abraham Lincoln	John Tyler
James Madison	George Washington

II. The Very First

1. When were the first bicycles seen in America?
2. When was the first auto race track built in the United States?
3. The first steam shovel was invented when?
4. When was the first successful helicopter flight?
5. When was the first United States artificial satellite placed in orbit?
6. When were the first television broadcasts of major league baseball games?
7. When was the first atomic explosion?
8. When was the American flag first flown from a warship?
9. When was the first escalator built?
10. When were the Boy Scouts first formed in the United States?

Use these dates for your answers.

1777	1838	1910	1939	1945
1819	1900	1910	1940	1958

III. Geography

1. What continent is straight south of Texas?
2. Which state in the United States is the farthest south?
3. What South American country has two capital cities?
4. If a ship sails through the Panama Canal from the Caribbean Sea toward the Pacific Ocean, what direction is it sailing?

5. What is the world's longest river?
6. What is the world's deepest lake?
7. What continent has the smallest population?
8. What is the lowest place on the earth's surface?
9. What United States state capital has the greatest population?
10. What is the world's smallest country?

IV. Nicknames

1. What state is called the Buckeye State?
2. Steel City is what American city?
3. Who was the Angel of the Battlefield?
4. What was a Peacemaker in the Old West?
5. What was the best-known nickname for George Herman Ruth?
6. What is the Rose Bowl?
7. The Queen City of the Plains is where?
8. What were Quaker Guns?
9. What was the real name of the ship nicknamed Old Ironsides?
10. What woman was nicknamed Little Sure Shot?

V. Sports Records

1. What baseball player hit a lifetime total of 714 home runs?
2. What baseball player hit 61 home runs in 1961?
3. What was the first car to reach 600 miles per hour?
4. Who led the National Basketball Association in scoring from 1960 through 1966?
5. From 1937 until 1949 one man was heavy-

weight boxing champion of the world. Who was he?

6. Who first ran a four-minute mile?
7. What is the world's record broad jump?
8. What was the biggest fish ever caught by rod and reel?
9. What race horse won the most money for its owner?
10. In the last fifty years what major league pitcher won the most games in one year?

42. IMPOSSIBLE!

Louis hated to do the evening dishes more than anything in the world. He would do just about anything to avoid that chore. One evening an idea popped into his head.

"Mom," he said, "I'll make a deal with you. I have a trick in mind which I can do but which you can't. If you are unable to do it and I can, I don't have to do dishes for a week. If you can do it then I promise not to complain about doing dishes for an entire month. Deal?"

"Deal," his mother answered.

"Here's the trick," Louis said. "Take a water glass, two dinner forks, and a half-dollar. Balance the forks and coin on the rim of the glass so that only the half-dollar touches the glass. The forks may not touch the glass in any manner."

His mother tried the trick and soon said, "Impossible!"

Louis soon proved his mother was wrong. Are you as clever as Louis?

93

43. TOTALLY IMPOSSIBLE!

When the time came again for Louis to do the dishes he had another stunt ready for his mother.

"Mom," he said, "I've got another trick you can't do but I can. Are you up to another bet?"

His mother hesitated a minute before replying. Then she said, "Tell me the trick first. I'm not sure I want to bet."

"I'll bet you I can cut a piece of paper which is three inches by five inches in such a way that I can step right through it."

"You mean you will put that paper over your feet and pull it up over your head?"

"That is what I mean," Louis answered.

"You will do this just by cutting the paper and when you put your feet through the paper it will still be joined at the ends?"

"Yes, that's right. When I put my feet through the paper there will be paper circling my entire body."

"Totally impossible!" declared his mother.

Louis didn't have to do dishes for another week! Can you prove you're a match for Louis?

44. THE LAST STRAW

No doubt you have heard people speak of something as being the "last straw." They meant something was just about more than they could stand. This puzzle may well be the "last straw" for you. For this reason it comes at the end of the book.

We are asking you to travel from "A" to "Z" in exactly twenty-six moves. Each time you cross a square is a move. You may move up and down or across the page but never on a diagonal. Each time you move into a new square that square must contain a letter of the alphabet you have not already used. When you have traveled from "A" to "Z" you will have crossed each letter of the alphabet one time and only one time. You will *not* cross these letters in order.

You may find this puzzle rather simple or you may feel it is impossible. It does have an answer but don't be too quick to peek. Work on it and if you are not able to solve it at first come back later and try it again.

A	B	C	O	Z	M	Y
F	K	T	L	K	G	D
W	M	B	S	L	C	P
V	P	O	Y	V	V	K
X	O	U	R	S	H	J
M	S	H	D	S	I	U
E	K	T	X	C	F	S
B	Q	E	T	I	J	U
F	D	R	P	N	Q	E
D	W	N	H	Q	G	Z

ANSWERS

1. WORD BOXES Page 1

I. STOP
   TAPE
   OPEN
   PENS

II. WEST
    ECHO
    SHUT
    TOTS

III. SLED
     LOVE
     EVEN
     DENT

IV. MINE
    IDEA
    NEWS
    EAST

V. DATE
   AREA
   TENS
   EASE

VI. LOST
    OBOE
    SODA
    TEAR

2. FOUR SQUARE Page 3

I. LIST
   ONLY
   STAR
   SOME

II. BALL
    OBOE
    ALAS
    TENT

III. FLED
     LIVE
     AMEN
     WENT

IV. CODE
    AREA
    VANS
    ELSE

V. SIDE
   ASIA
   FLAT
   EELS

VI. CLOD
    LAKE
    ACRE
    PEAR

3. MONKEY MATH Page 8

^{1}1	^{2}2	^{3}5		^{4}9	^{5}9	^{6}9
^{7}4	0	^{8}1	^{9}2		^{10}5	6
^{11}4		^{12}1	4	6	^{13}1	^{14}0
	^{15}3	^{16}6			^{17}3	^{18}7
	^{19}6	1			^{20}2	2
^{21}4		^{22}2	^{23}6	^{24}1	3	^{25}3
^{26}3	^{27}8		^{28}6	4	^{29}4	8
^{30}4	4	^{31}9			^{32}5	4	7

4. STAIRSTEPS Page 11

I. 1. over
    2. shut
    3. thin
    4. hero
    OHIO

II. 1. miner
    2. canoe
    3. crime
    4. front
    5. maybe
    MAINE

III. 1. nephew
     2. second
     3. review
     4. female
     5. guards
     6. Canada
     NEVADA

97

IV. 1. fashion   V. 1. interest
     2. glisten   2. platinum
        or glitter   3. goldfish
     3. crooked   4. radiator
     4. startle   5. Seminole
     5. provide   6. railroad
     6. outside   7. magnolia
     7. America   8. teachers
     FLORIDA   ILLINOIS

5. VOCABULARY CHECK   Page 14

1. Napsack
2. Non-skid pancake
3. Stamping ground
4. Knightgown
5. Sick shooter
6. Wet pets
7. One who is fed up with people
8. Thirst aid station
9. Car's life story
10. Person with the gift of grab
11. Night watchman
12. Witch watch
13. Top secret
14. Flying hypodermic needle
15. Prince of Wails

7. THE LOSER   Page 16

The following solution is one of several possible.

X	X	X	X	
X		X	X	X
	X	■	X	X
X	X		X	X
X	X	X		X

8. AN EXALTATION OF LARKS Page 17

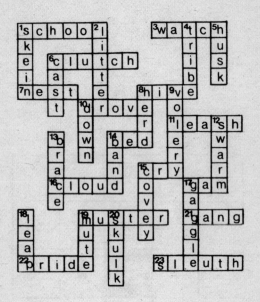

9. ONLY FOR THOSE WITH SHARP EYES Page 20

The letter "Q" does not appear in the jumble.

10. **THAT'S ENGLISH** Page 20

1. petrol
2. flat
3. nappies
4. sweets
5. lift
6. lorries
7. chemist's
8. telly
9. chips
10. dustman
11. ladders
12. porter
13. wireless
14. bonnet
15. boot
16. serviette
17. underground
18. fridge
19. ring up
20. queue
21. minced beef
22. cot
23. flannel
24. hoover
25. post

11. CAN YOU COUNT? Page 22

The authors found 40 squares: 8 small; 18 regular; 9 measuring 2 by 2 regular squares; 4 measuring 3 by 3; 1 measuring 4 by 4.

12. LIFE IS A RIDDLE Page 23

1. Shoplifters
2. We grow older.
3. Two boys practicing their trumpets
4. One is hard to get up; the other is hard to get down.
5. A leg (or a ruler)
6. Good-bye, at last I've met my match.
7. She ran from the ball.
8. It goes to waist.
9. Three strikes and you're out.
10. Neither — use a spoon if you wish to be correct.
11. The English Channel
12. There was a lot less to learn.
13. Are you going out tonight?
14. Nothing. It just shut up.
15. They both run.
16. A coat of paint
17. Between you and me there's something that smells.
18. Chicken of the sea
19. Ice
20. Wise quacker
21. They make Ma mad.
22. He goes to the Batroom.

23. She used a pencil.
24. An orphan
25. An aunt-eater

13. MUSIC MAKERS   Page 24

1. Flute
2. French horn
3. Tuba
4. Bassoon
5. Trumpet
6. Clarinet
7. Kettledrum
8. Oboe
9. Trombone
10. Bass drum
11. Saxophone
12. Violin
13. Cymbals

14. LETTER MAZES   Page 25

I. West of the Mississippi — Twenty-four states

Alaska	Kansas	North Dakota
Arizona	Louisiana	Oklahoma
Arkansas	Minnesota	Oregon
California	Missouri	South Dakota
Colorado	Montana	Texas
Hawaii	Nebraska	Utah
Idaho	Nevada	Washington
Iowa	New Mexico	Wyoming

II. Major U.S. Cities — Twenty-five cities in order of size

New York	Washington, D.C.	St. Louis
Chicago	Indianapolis	New Orleans
Los Angeles	Cleveland	Phoenix
Philadelphia	Milwaukee	Columbus
Detroit	San Francisco	Seattle
Houston	San Diego	Jacksonville
Baltimore	San Antonio	Denver
Dallas	Boston	Pittsburgh
	Memphis	

III. United States Presidents — in order (Cleveland's second term omitted)

Washington	Hayes
Adams	Garfield
Jefferson	Arthur
Madison	Cleveland
Monroe	Harrison
Adams	McKinley
Jackson	Roosevelt
Van Buren	Taft
Harrison	Wilson
Tyler	Harding
Polk	Coolidge
Taylor	Hoover
Fillmore	Roosevelt
Pierce	Truman
Buchanan	Eisenhower
Lincoln	Kennedy
Johnson	Johnson
	Nixon

15. BEGINNER'S NUMBER CROSS Page 29

5	2	1		6	3	9
5		4	5	7		1
8	2	6		2	8	4
	7				2	
4	6	2		5	3	7
9		7	4	0		9
1	5	8		3	0	1

16. NUMBER CROSS Page 30

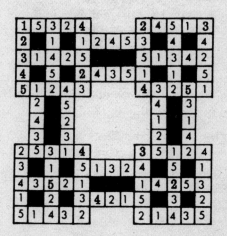

105

17. SHORTIES FOR SHARPIES Page 31

1. December and January
2. Good
3. They didn't play each other.
4. A stamp collector
5. The two mothers were a grandmother and a mother. The two daughters were the mother (the grandmother's daughter) and her daughter.
6. Three minutes
7. Forty pounds
8. One hour
9. Neither — it is Frankfort.
10. Ninety
11. The mayor is her sister.
12. All have twenty-eight days in them.
13. It has no actual size. It is a point only.
14. We would suggest the match first.
15. Eight minutes for the four necessary cuts
16. Living men are not buried.
17. Six-dozen dozen equal 864 while half a dozen dozen equal only 72.
18. Four
19. $5\frac{1}{3}$
20. Fifty-five
21. Oboe
22. Ohio and Iowa
23. One
24. Incorrectly
25. Ben Franklin, of course

18. STARS IN YOUR EYES Page 33

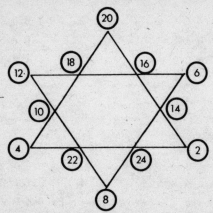

19. STATE NICKNAMES Page 34

1. California
2. Nevada
3. Nebraska
4. Texas
5. Kentucky
6. New York
7. North Carolina
8. Indiana
9. Arizona
10. Louisiana
11. South Carolina
12. Tennessee
13. Alaska
14. Vermont
15. New Jersey

CENTENNIAL STATE

20. MISSING MATH Page 35

1.
```
      3 4 6
      5 1 8
  +   4 9 2
    1 3 5 6
```

2.
```
    1 3 0 0 4
  −   8 6 5 1
      4 3 5 3
```

3.
```
    1 2 3 4
    ×    5
    6 1 7 0
```

4.
```
        2 1 6 2
    3) 6 4 8 6
       6
       ‾
         4
         3
         ‾
         1 8
         1 8
         ‾‾
             6
             6
             ‾
```

5.
```
        9 0 4 6
        ×   2 3
      2 7 1 3 8
    1 8 0 9 2
    2 0 8 0 5 8
```

6.
```
          3 0 5
        × 7 5 4
        1 2 2 0
        1 5 2 5
      2 1 3 5
      2 2 9 9 7 0
```

108

21. DOG SHOW Page 36

1. Saint Bernard
2. Great Dane
3. Norwegian Elkhound
4. Irish Wolfhound
5. Scottish Terrier
6. Labrador Retriever
7. Brittany Spaniel
8. Cocker Spaniel
9. Boston Terrier
10. Bull Mastiff
11. Doberman Pinscher
12. German Shepherd
13. Siberian Husky
14. Irish Setter
15. Golden Retriever
16. Rhodesian Ridgeback
17. Welsh Corgi
18. Old English Sheep Dog
19. Fox Terrier
20. Great Pyrenees

23. MATHEMAGIC Page 39

I. You should find your phone number followed by your age in the answer.

II. Your answer is 6.

III. You are now back to your starting number.

IV. Again, you are back to your starting number.

V. Your age and the number you added in step six appear in that order.

VI. You have the number of years of school

V. Your age and the number you added in step six appear in that order.

VI. You have the number of years of school you have completed.

VII. Your answer is one.
VIII. Your answer shows your house number and age.
IX. Once more, you are back where you started.
X. Your answer contains the numbers you chose in steps one and five.

24. CAPITAL CROSS-UP Page 42

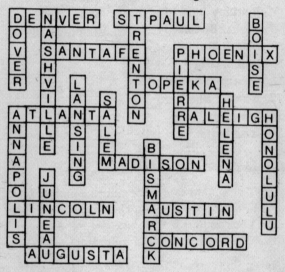

25. MAGIC SUBTRACTION TRIANGLE
Page 44

```
     4                    6                    9
   8   7                2   7                3   1
  1   3                4   5                5   6
 5 9 2 6              3 8 1 9              8 4 2 7
   0                    3                    9
   —                    —                    —
```

110

26. YOU'VE GOT TO BE KIDDING!
Page 45

2	30	28	8
24	12	14	18
16	20	22	10
26	6	4	32

27. CODES FOR CODEBREAKERS
Page 46

1. I only regret that I have but one life to lose for my country. Nathan Hale

2. Never leave that till tomorrow which you can do today. Benjamin Franklin

3. A house divided against itself cannot stand. Abraham Lincoln

4. There is such a thing as a man being too proud to fight. Woodrow Wilson

5. The only thing we have to fear is fear itself. Franklin Delano Roosevelt

28. ALPHABETICS Page 47

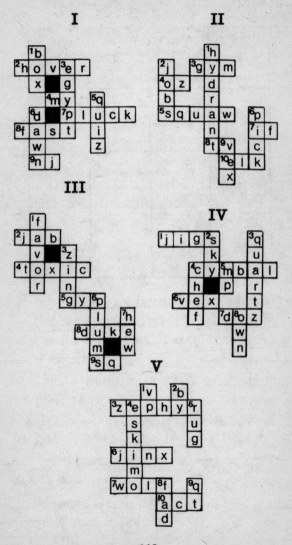

I

II

III

IV

V

112

29. BAKER'S DOZEN   Page 51

1. One
2. Bob has seven; John five.
3. Twenty-five
4. Eighteen
5. One half-dollar, thirty-nine dimes, and sixty pennies
6. Twelve
7. Your last answer should have been 4,100. Was it 5,000 by any chance?
8. Joke, folks, Coke, the white of an egg (certainly not yolk, which is the yellow part of the egg)
9. Joe has twenty-five; Lloyd thirty-five.
10. Bob is $10\frac{1}{2}$ and Mary $\frac{1}{2}$.
11. 40, 3, 2, 16
12. 8, 14, 18, 32
13. To keep his pigs in, we suspect.

30. HOW ABOUT THAT!   Page 54

1. $99\frac{9}{9}$
2. $99\frac{99}{99}$
3. $3\frac{3}{3}$
4. $3 \div \frac{3}{3}$
5. $\frac{1}{1}$
6. $11 + 1\frac{1}{11}$
7. $5\frac{5}{5}$
8. $(8 - 8) \times 8$
9. $7 + 7 \div .7$
10. $\dfrac{333 - 33}{3}$

11. 44
    444
      4
      4
      4

12. $10 \times 10 + 10 \div 10 - 10$

31. COWBOY WORDS Page 54

1. Cayuse	10. Reata	19. Dogie
2. Hole up	11. Hombre	20. Lariat
3. Wrangler	12. Mustang	21. Frijoles
4. Equalizer	13. Tally	22. Sombrero
5. Rustle	14. Arroyo	23. Hoss
6. Adios	15. Bust	24. Lope
7. Necktie Party	16. Puncher	25. Rodeo
8. Calaboose	17. Critter	
9. Chuck	18. Remuda	

32. QUICK NOW! Page 56

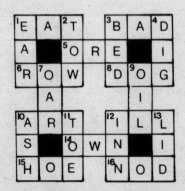

114

33. DIAMOND IN THE ROUGH Page 57

I	II	III	IV
1. be	1. at	1. it	1. he
2. bed	2. cat	2. sit	2. she
3. bend	3. coat	3. site	3. shed
4. blend	4. coast	4. stile	4. shade
5. lend	5. cost	5. stifle	5. head
6. end	6. cot	6. files	6. had
7. en	7. to	7. life	7. ad
		8. fie	
		9. if	

V	VI	VII	VIII
1. an	1. am	1. ag	1. la
2. pan	2. mar	2. gat	2. ale
3. pant	3. cram	3. gate	3. gale
4. pants	4. cream	4. stage	4. angel
5. plants	5. scream	5. grates	5. Angles
6. slant	6. reams	6. strange	6. tangles
7. last	7. seam	7. ranges	7. strangle
8. sat	8. sea	8. anger	8. strange
9. as	9. es	9. rage	9. grants
		10. are	10. trans
		11. re	11. rant
			12. rat
			13. Ra

34. DOUBLE TROUBLE Page 63

I	II	III	IV	V	VI
rabbit	giggle	follow	tassel	rattle	muzzle
rabble	wiggle	bellow	vessel	settle	puzzle
rubber	goggle	fillet	basset	tattle	fizzle
rubble	haggle	bullet	lesson	tattoo	sizzle
ribbon	logger	mullet	fossil	battle	guzzle
robber	maggot	pullet	mussel	better	dazzle

35. MIND BINDERS Page 65

I. Scrambled Occupations

Joe is a painter and barber, Dick is a musician and storekeeper, and Bob is a gardener and butler.

II. Clever Thieves

The thieves placed the planks at the corner of the ditch in the following manner.

III. On the Road to St. Ives

The traveler was going to St. Ives.

IV. Busy Bus

The bus made six stops.

V. Hunting in the Dark

If the hunter chose any three socks he would be safe.

VI. A Rocky Problem

Larry and his helper buried the boulder and removed the dirt.

116

VII. Large Inheritance
The uncle drew the following picture to explain.

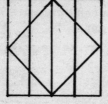

The four triangular pieces of land may be sold without breaking the terms of the will.

VIII. Ship and Ladder
The twenty-fourth step will still be just above the water. As the ship moves up with the rising water so does the ladder, which is attached to the ship.

IX. Drawing Exercise

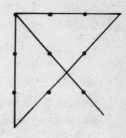

X. What a Lot of Handshaking
Twenty-eight handshakes should do the job.

XI. They Are Relatives
The fellow at the well was the farmer's son.

XII. Train Travel
When the two trains meet they will be the same distance from Boston.

XIII. That's a Crazy Way to Measure Water

One gallon: Fill the 3-gallon bucket and empty it into the 5-gallon bucket. Refill the 3 and empty it into the 5 until the 5 is full. What is left in the 3 is one gallon.

Two gallons: Fill the 5 and from it fill the 3. What is left in the 5 will equal two gallons.

Three gallons: Fill the 3-gallon bucket, of course.

Four gallons: Fill the 5 and from it fill the 3. Pour out the 3 and empty the remainder of the 5 into the 3. Now refill the 5. Pour enough from the 5 to finish filling the 3, and what is left in the 5 totals four gallons.

Five gallons: Need we say to fill the 5?

Six gallons: Fill the 3 and empty it into the 5. Refill the 3 and you now have six gallons.

Seven gallons: Fill the 5 and from it fill the 3. Empty the 3. Now pour what is left in the 5 into the 3 and refill the 5 for a total of seven gallons.

Eight gallons: Fill both buckets, of course.

XIV. That's Easy
12,111

XV. What a Question!
Are you asleep?

XVI. That's a Belt?
Strangely enough, the new belt would only have to be six and a fraction of an inch longer than the old one.

XVII. Is There Such a Word?
Underground

XVIII. What About This Word?
Sequoia

XIX. Lunch Date
Brown wore black, Green wore brown, and Black wore green.

XX. That's an Order!
The digits are in alphabetical order.

36. DESIGNOGRAMS   Page 74

I	II	III	IV
1. ease	1. onto	1. arena	1. erode
2. edge	2. food	2. canal	2. level
3. meet	3. Oslo	3. plane	3. break
4. feet	4. boot	4. Japan	4. fever
5. eave	5. oleo	5. aloha	5. erase
6. else			

V	VI	
1. algebra	1. ate	8. typist
2. amoeba	2. tot	9. stilts
3. aroma	3. text	10. settle
4. area	4. twist	11. starts
5. alpha	5. match	12. turret
6. armada	6. state	13. tempest
7. alfalfa	7. tempt	14. turncoat
		15. turbulent

119

37. THE UNHAPPY GROCER Page 79

1. apple, peach, pear
2. carrot, corn, spinach
3. celery, pea, squash
4. cucumber, lettuce, onion
5. lemon, lime, orange
6. apricot, cherry, plum
7. parsnip, tomato, turnip
8. date, fig, olive
9. grapefruit, persimmon, tangerine
10. asparagus, rutabaga, yam

38. JUMBLES Page 80

I. Ten State Names
Ohio, Colorado, Montana, Florida, Maine, Vermont, Idaho, Iowa, Missouri, New Mexico

II. Twelve Colors
pink, yellow, purple, violet, crimson, orange, brown, white, black, green, gray, blue

III. African Safari — Twelve Animals
lion, zebra, buffalo, elephant, rhino, gorilla, hippo, monkey, ostrich, giraffe, python, eland

39. THINKIES Page 82

I. Old Friends
Bill's old friend was the girl's mother whose name was Mary.

II. Poor J.C. Richards

The rule infraction was committed by J.C.'s jockey.

III. Beloved Librarian

Thelma was in the record department (or the microfilm department if you wish) of the library.

IV. Poor Stella

Stella was a secretary, not a teacher, so her salary was not the same.

V. Border Guard

Willy was a guard on the western side of the Wall. The escapees were from the eastern side coming toward Willy.

VI. Overpaid?

Captain Burnell was a Navy captain, which is a higher rank than that of major.

VII. London Smog

The elderly man was blind. The smog made no difference to him.

VIII. Funny Farm

Clarence operated a fish farm. He planted fingerlings, not seeds.

IX. A Killer is Loose

The high wire artist who fell to his death was a trained chimp. Thus the killer could not be charged with murder or manslaughter.

X. Wild Ride

Johnny was driving an ambulance bringing an accident victim to the hospital.

40. HIDEOUTS   Page 89

1. manages
2. legal
3. sat, attack
4. father, form
5. asp, dislike
6. stripe
7. smart
8. eclipse
9. medial
10. land, diesel, tint, estate

41. QUIZ TIME   Page 90

I. American Presidents

1. John Tyler had fifteen children.
2. Abraham Lincoln was six feet four inches tall.
3. James Madison was only five feet four inches.
4. William Howard Taft weighed between 300 and 330 pounds.
5. Theodore Roosevelt became President when he was forty-two years old.
6. James Buchanan didn't marry.
7. William Henry Harrison was President only thirty-one days before his death.
8. Franklin D. Roosevelt was President for twelve years and thirty-nine days.
9. John Adams lived until he was ninety.
10. George Washington's second inaugural address had only 135 words.

II. The Very First
1. Velocipedes or "swift walkers" were first seen in New York in 1819.
2. A board-covered auto raceway was built in 1910 near Los Angeles, California.
3. In 1838 William Otis invented the steam shovel.
4. Igor Sikorsky made a fifteen-minute flight 'on July 18, 1940.
5. Explorer I was lanuched January 31, 1958, from Cape Canaveral (now Cape Kennedy), Florida.
6. In August of 1939 the Cincinnati Reds played the Brooklyn Dodgers before two TV cameras.
7. On July 16, 1945, the world's first atomic explosion occurred at Alamogordo Air Base in New Mexico.
8. John Paul Jones flew the Stars and Stripes on the *Ranger,* July 4, 1777.
9. In 1900 an escalator was built in New York for the Paris Exposition.
10. In 1910 America's first Scouts were organized in the District of Columbia.

III. Geography
1. Antarctica is directly south of Texas.
2. Hawaii lies farther south than Florida.
3. Bolivia's capitals are LaPaz and Sucre.
4. It sails southeast while in the Panama Canal.
5. The Nile in Africa is the longest.
6. Lake Baikal in Siberia is the the deepest.

7. Antarctica has no population except for expeditions.
8. The Dead Sea between Israel and Jordan is 1,286 feet below sea level.
9. Indianapolis, Indiana, has about 750,000 population. Boston's metropolitan area is much larger, but not the city proper.
10. Monaco covers less than one square mile.

IV. Nicknames
1. Ohio
2. Pittsburgh, Pennsylvania
3. Clara Barton
4. A revolver
5. Babe Ruth
6. Pasadena Stadium in California
7. Denver, Colorado
8. Logs painted to look like cannon
9. *Constitution*
10. Annie Oakley

V. Sports Records
1. Babe Ruth holds this record.
2. Roger Maris set this record while playing for the New York Yankees.
3. On November 15, 1965, *Spirit of America* ran just over 600 miles per hour.
4. Wilt Chamberlain was the leader. His best year was 1962 when he scored 4,029 points for Philadelphia.
5. Joe Louis held the heavyweight championship longer than any other boxer.
6. In 1954 Britain's Roger Bannister ran a mile in six tenths of a second less than four minutes.

7. A jump of 29 feet $2\frac{1}{4}$ inches was made by Bob Beamon in the 1968 Olympics.
8. In 1964 a 1,780 pound tiger shark was caught off the coast of South Carolina.
9. Kelso won $1,977,896 during his racing career.
10. In 1934 Dizzy Dean of the St. Louis Cardinals won 34 games.

42. IMPOSSIBLE! Page 93

Slip the half-dollar into the fork tines as shown. Rest the coin on the rim of the glass so the coin extends out over the table. Move the forks gently back and forth until it balances.

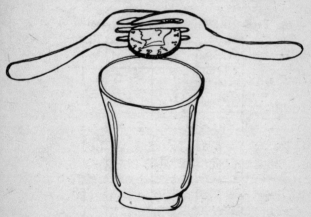

The fork handles come back on either side of the glass. The coin and two forks appear to "hang" in space over the rim of the glass. Only a tiny fraction of the coin actually touches the rim of the glass.

43. TOTALLY IMPOSSIBLE! Page 94

Begin by folding the paper double. Then cut the paper as shown. Finally cut along the center fold on all but the two outside edges. Carefully stretch the paper into a large circle and step through it.

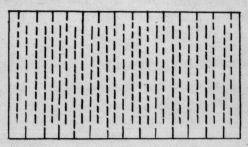

44. THE LAST STRAW   Page 94

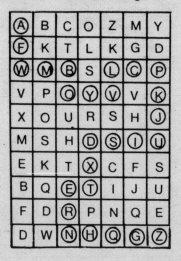

126